Wet Feet

Written by Roderick Hunt
Illustrated by Alex Brychta

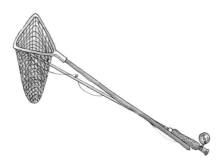

OXFORD
UNIVERSITY PRESS

Read these words

deep   feed

feel   need

reel   weed

feet   eel

Wilf had a rod and a net.

Wilf and Dad got to the river.

"We can fish in that bit,"
said Dad.

"Let's get fishing," said Wilf.

9

"Let's feed the fish," said Dad.

"I can feel a fish," said Wilf.

"Reel it in, then," said Dad.

It was not a fish. It was a lot
of weed.

"I can feel a fish," said Dad.

Dad got his feet wet.

Wilf got his feet wet.

"Get the net," said Dad.

It was an eel.

Dad let the eel go.

"We got an eel and wet feet," said Wilf. "But no fish."

Talk about the story

Where did Wilf and Dad go fishing?

What did they catch?

How did they get wet feet?

What do you like doing at the weekend?

Jumbled letters

Make the *ee* words.